GUITAR STYLES: ROCK

BRIAN MAY

COMPILED AND EDITED BY MICHAEL STIMPSON

C000124599

CONTENTS

Guitar Styles! is a new concept in guitar publishing—it gives you the chance to stretch your skills and learn Bass, Classical, Flamenco, Folk, Jazz, and Rock styles, using your own instrument.

There are hints from each composer on how to achieve the authentic sound of each style.

Whether you're a beginner or more experienced guitarist, a teacher or student, this is the series for you to try some new solos and to play the ensemble pieces with your friends.

Why not try *Guitar Styles! Bass* next?

6542611

BEDFORDSHIRE
LEISURE
SERVICES
COUNTY COUNCIL

N

M 787·615
MAY

Music Department
OXFORD UNIVERSITY PRESS
Oxford and New York

Oxford University Press, Walton Street, Oxford OX2 6DP
© Oxford University Press 1994
Photocopying this copyright material is ILLEGAL

Designed by Paul Cleal
Cover designed by Rowie Christopher
Music engraved by Barnes Music Engraving Ltd.
Printed in Great Britain by Caligraving Ltd.

INTRODUCTION

Because the post-fifties electric guitar, like the violin, is played using notes which can be placed anywhere between semitones (i.e. at pitches unrelated to a diatonic scale), musical notation cannot truly represent how I, for instance, play these pieces. Of course no two people would play them the same anyway, which to me is part of the joy of the rock guitar. Don't try to stick too rigidly to the chords; make the pieces your own. I hope these notes provide a few 'jumping off' points for your development as a guitar player.

Good luck!!

Brian May

NOTES ON TECHNIQUE

The Eton Chugging Song

The bass guitar is the main instrument at first, with the 'chugging' lead guitar creating a backdrop. First turn the volume up so that if the strings are open (not damped) when hit, the notes will sustain and be distorted. A tighter rhythmic feel is required here however, so damp the strings using the side of the right hand at the bridge, thus reducing the sustain and distortion, and giving shorter notes. Drag the pick quickly across the adjacent strings so that they sound simultaneously. The 'chugging' effect should be uneven in strength, some of the notes stroked gently and others emphasized or accented. A touch of echo also helps. Be careful to damp the remaining strings with the left hand so that they do not vibrate in sympathy. The first finger of the left hand can be laid flat across the strings or the shape of a C chord (with bar) may be used. More volume and distortion can be added in bar 9 where the lead guitar takes over, but a cleaner sound is required for the contrasting passage between bars 21 and 27.

Who Wants to Live Forever

Originally written for the film 'Highlander', this piece was later adapted to be the flagship song for the British Bone Marrow Donor Appeal. The version for this collection is light in texture, and the tone settings should be clean. It demonstrates that a player does not have to bend notes all the time in order to put emotion into a piece; good use of vibrato, slides and snaps will achieve this. The change from arpeggio (broken chord) accompaniment to full, strummed chords in bar 37 helps to drive the piece to its climax.

The Squeeze

'The Squeeze' involves string-bending, the technique of pressing a string at one fret and squeezing (bending) it so that the pitch rises, usually by a semitone or a tone (one or two frets). A new note is created and at the beginning of the piece the sound of the original note rising should be discernable. A string-bend is indicated by a broken square bracket ⌐ ‒ ‒ ‒ ‒ ¬ , and a notehead (without a tail) shows the fret to be pressed. Sometimes a string may be pre-bent so that when it is played, only the note falling to the fretted note is heard. A note head (without a tail and in brackets) is used to indicate this. A string is normally squeezed towards the lower-sounding strings, i.e. the second string should be pushed towards the third string and so on. Left-hand fingering is important, and to make it a little easier, other left-hand fingers may be used to help push the string. Vibrato ⁓ may be added to a squeezed note by squeezing and releasing the string still further, and more quickly.

Ice Dance

This resembles a short Spanish piece from the album 'Innuendo', which begins in a similar way. 'Ice Dance' moves the melody in a different direction and creates an old-fashioned type of piece for electric guitar. Give both guitar parts a clean sound. Select the pick-up nearest to the fingerboard for the top-guitar part, and keep the amplifier settings down. A little reverb will highlight the harmonic aspects of the melody. Keep the ensemble tight by maintaining good control of the rhythm.

Oil Slick

The short introduction is played in first position. Bar 7 gives a similar chugging effect as in 'The Eton Chugging Song'. Some 'cries' from the guitar follow, which involve string-bending and 'double snaps' (bars 12–14). Here, two strings are covered by the third left-hand finger, squeezed (bent) by that finger and then snapped off to a small half-bar of the first finger. The main piece begins in bar 15 and uses chords, runs containing some hammer-ons, and an adaptation of the 'cries' from the introduction. These are built up by keeping one note the same, and squeezing another up and down—a device borrowed from country music. The final section (from bar 31), requires short slides from the lead guitar, and some damping.

Brian's Blues

The blues feeling is produced by using the technique of squeezing notes (see the notes for 'The Squeeze'). However, 'Brian's Blues' is slower, and the squeeze to the upper note should also be slower. The piece moves in and out of the major and minor keys, and the basic blues sequence has been truncated. Play it with a fairly hard-driven tone, but without too much distortion. The sound then moves between that of low amplification and the somewhat distorted tone of B.B. King, but should not have the full-blown sound of Jimi Hendrix. Aim for a lazy 'Sunday afternoon' feel.

Green Piece

This piece is more suitable for two steel-string guitars or two nylon-strung Spanish guitars, as it does not contain any sounds or techniques that are intrinsically electric. String-bending should be used sparingly, but vibrato is effective. Use a pick for the melody line, although on a steel-strung guitar the fingers (not nails) give a good sound. Shorten some of the notes (staccato) to contrast and lift the melody, by moving one of your right-hand fingers lightly on to the string that has been sounded. Keep a good balance between the two parts—the chords need to be heard but must never dominate the piece.

Brian May and Michael Stimpson

BRIAN MAY AND MICHAEL STIMPSON

The Eton Chugging Song

Play the introduction rhythmically, but allow the bass to stand out when it begins. More distortion can then be added to the lead guitar, although this should be cleaned up for the central section of broken chords. Take it quite fast.

© Oxford University Press 1994

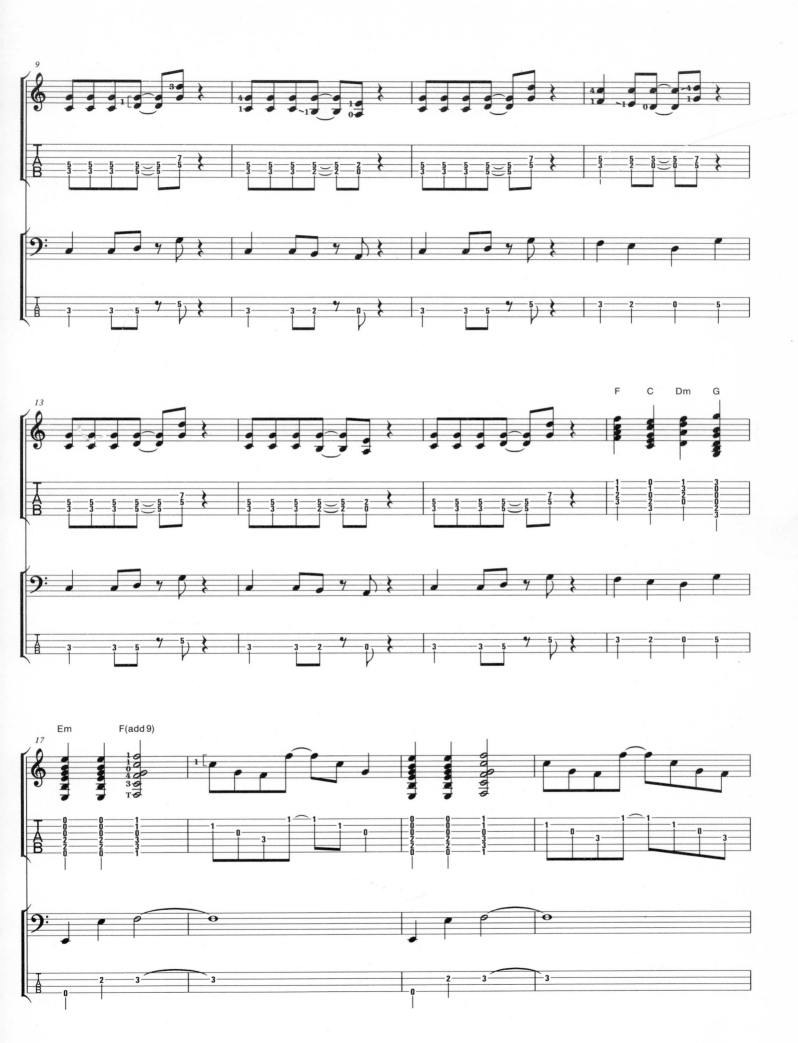

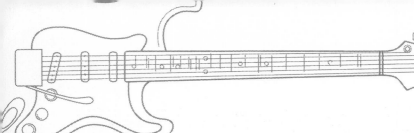

Who Wants to Live Forever

Set the tone of the guitars to make a clean sound, and use vibrato and slides to add feeling.
Control the volume with care, as the music builds strongly towards the end.

© Oxford University Press 1994

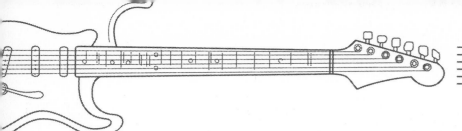

BRIAN MAY AND MICHAEL STIMPSON

The Squeeze

The lead line has a mixture of string-bending, slurs, and vibrato, so take it easy at first. Aim for something that sounds relaxed and fluent, even at the faster tempos.

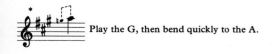

Play the G, then bend quickly to the A.

© Oxford University Press 1994

17

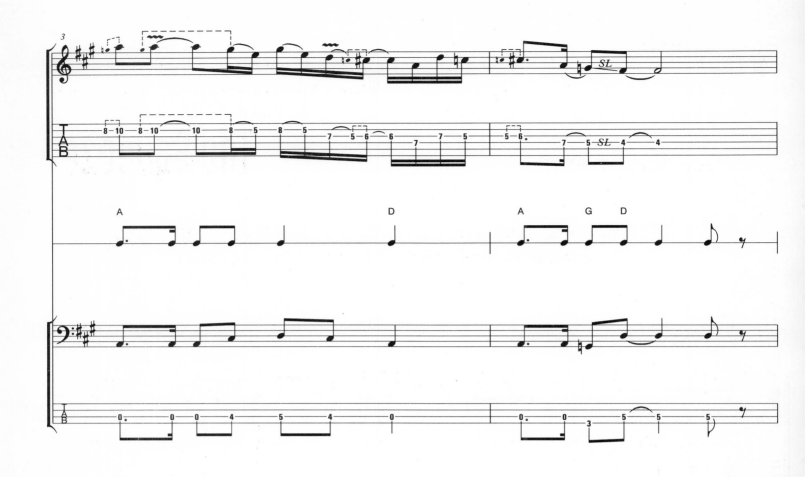

19

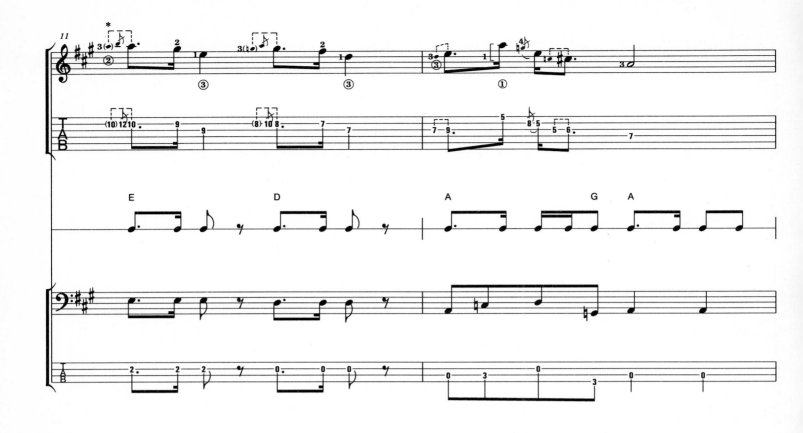

Fret the A, pre-bend to B, play the B and release the bend to sound the A.

21

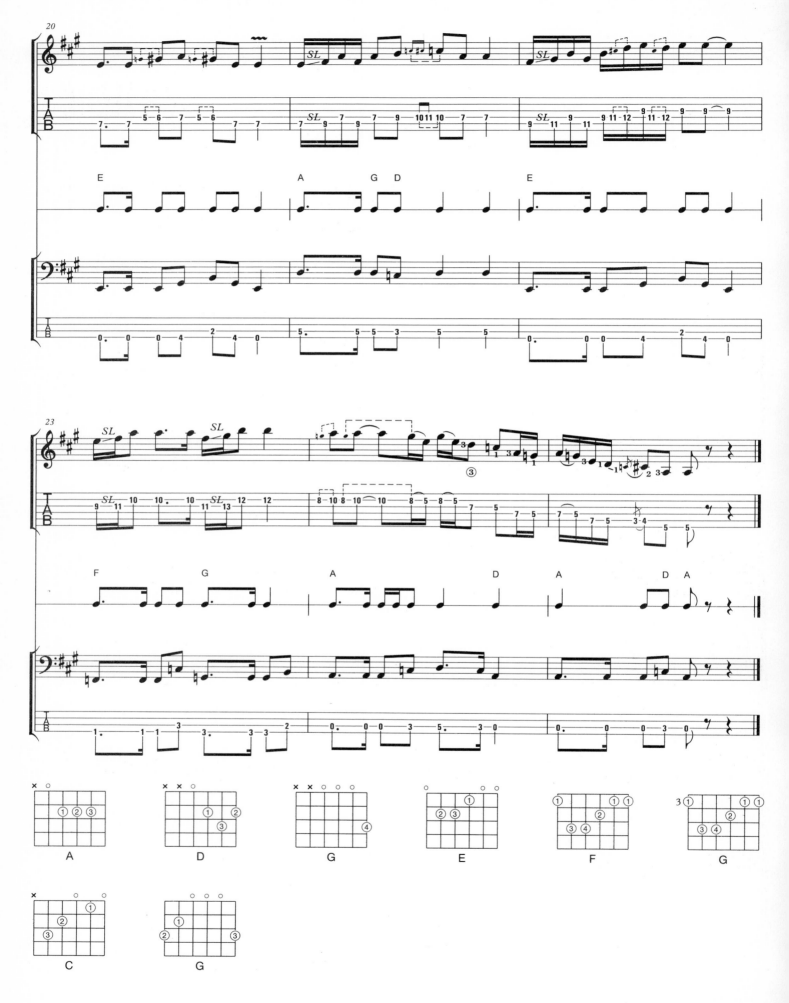

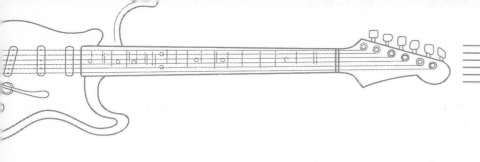

Ice Dance

Use a clean sound to play the piece, select the front pick-up and avoid distortion. Some reverb will help and the melody should be played smoothly.

© Oxford University Press 1994

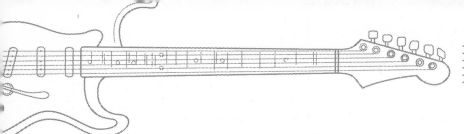

BRIAN MAY AND MICHAEL STIMPSON

Oil Slick

Play the introduction quite freely and with a ringing sound. Some chugging follows, as used in 'The Eton Chugging Song', but after that the sound should be strong and dirty.

© Oxford University Press 1994

29

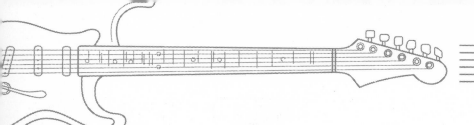

Brian's Blues

Take it fairly slowly to give the lazy feel of the blues, and do not squeeze the notes too quickly. Use a hard-driven tone but without too much distortion.

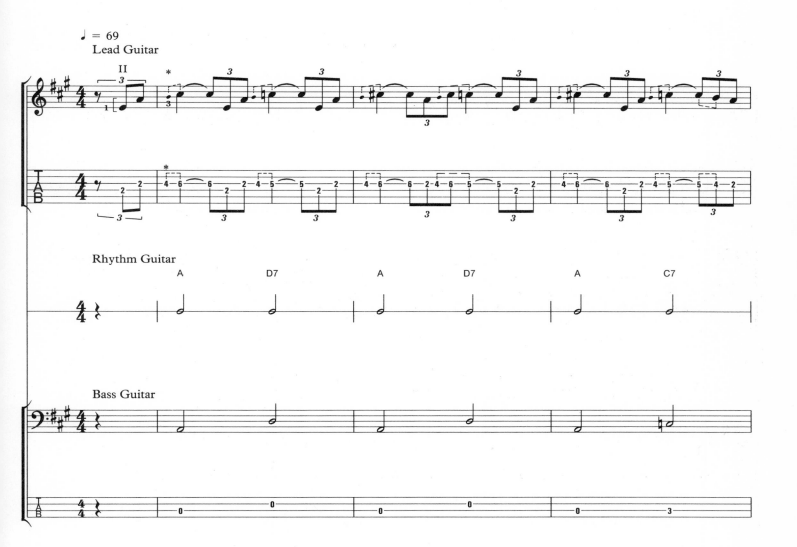

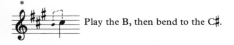
Play the B, then bend to the C♯.

© Oxford University Press 1994

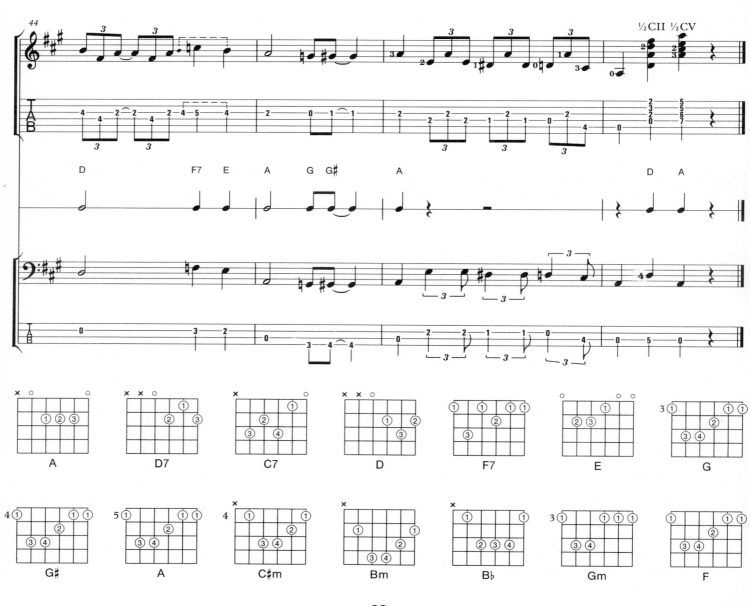

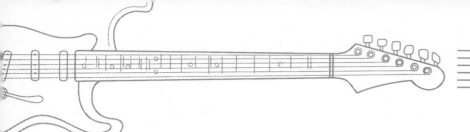

BRIAN MAY AND MICHAEL STIMPSON

Green Piece

Use either a pick or fingers for playing the melody line, but whichever you use make sure that it stands out above the chords. An easy-going tempo will be fine.

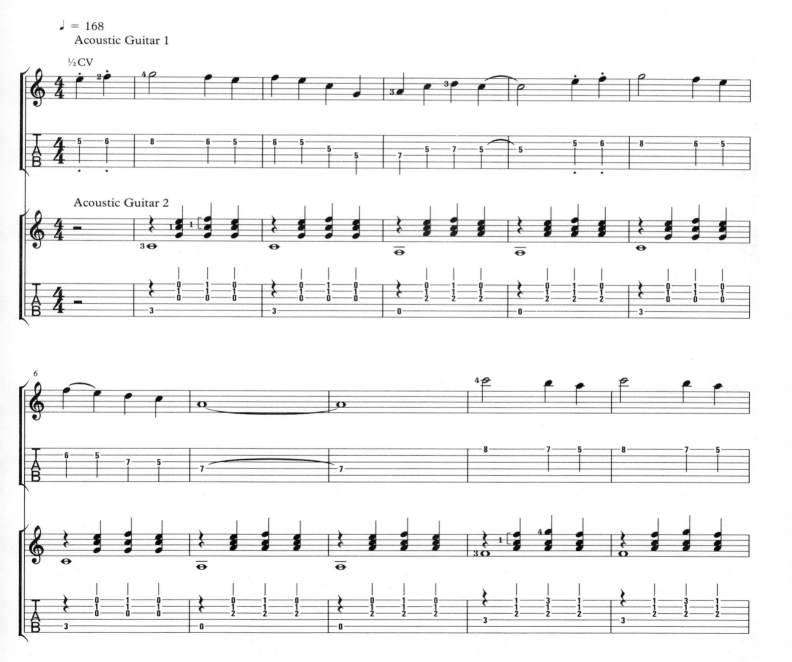

© Oxford University Press 1994

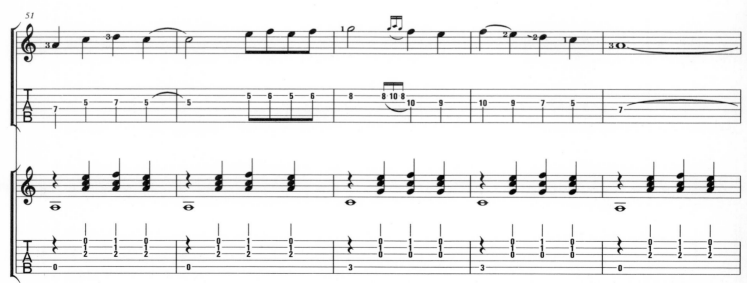

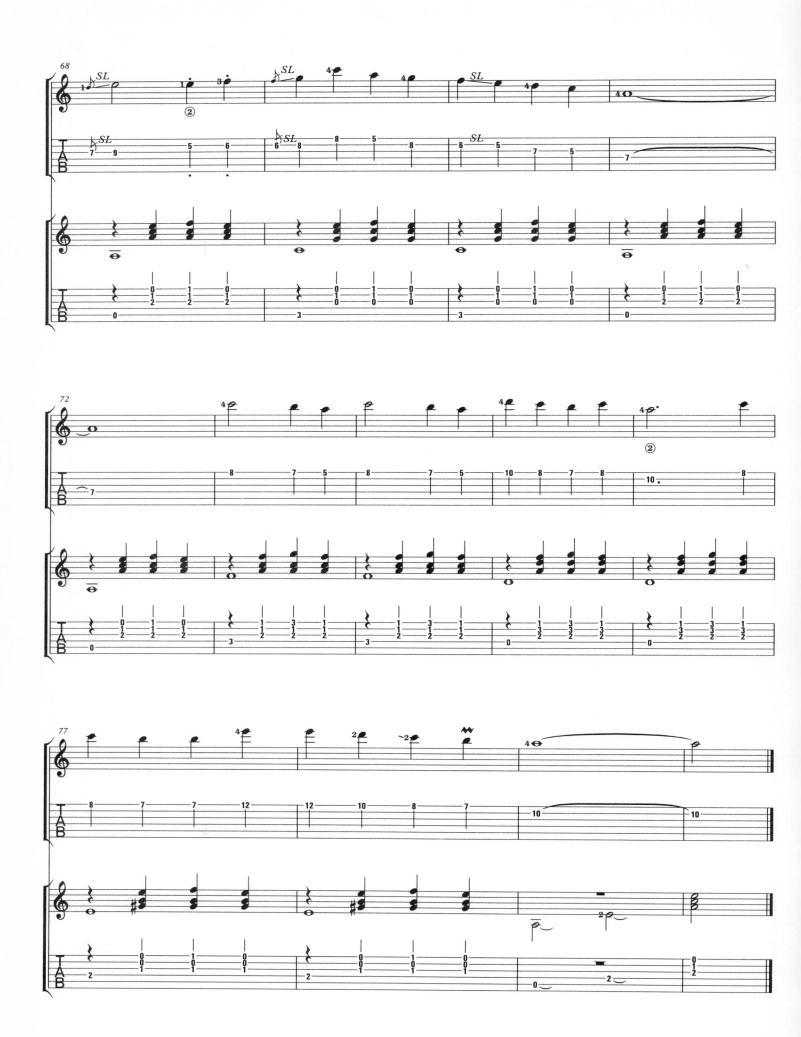

GENERAL INFORMATION

Open Strings

Electric Guitar

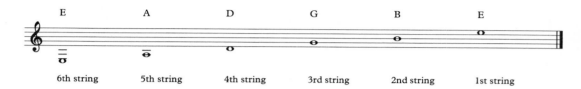

6th string 5th string 4th string 3rd string 2nd string 1st string

Bass Guitar

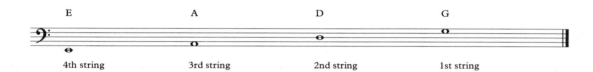

4th string 3rd string 2nd string 1st string

String Numbers

A number set in a circle indicates the string

- ① first string
- ⑥ sixth string

Fingering (Left Hand)

- 1 index finger
- 2 middle finger
- 3 ring finger
- 4 little finger
- T thumb

Bar and Half-Bar

For a bar chord the first finger is laid flat across all of the strings. It is indicated by the letter C. For a half-bar the first finger is laid flat across three or four strings. It is indicated by ½ C.

- CII Bar of the second fret
- ½CV Half-Bar of the fifth fret

Harmonics

Harmonics are indicated by a diamond-shaped note ♩. A number placed above the note shows the fret at which it is found.

- *Harm. 12* Harmonic at fret 12
- *Harm. 7* Harmonic at fret 7

Slides

A slide is indicated by a short diagonal line and 'SL' (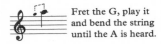). This should be distinguished from a 'finger-shift' which is shown by a diagonal line alone.

String Bend

A string bend is indicated by a broken square bracket (⌐¯¯¯¯¯¬).

Fret the G, play it
and bend the string
until the A is heard.

Vibrato

Vibrato is indicated thus: ∿

Tablature

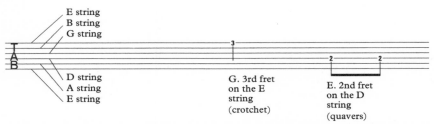

A number indicates which fret should be pressed. The line on which the number is placed shows the string. Rhythm is indicated by the note tails.

Chord Diagrams

Ex. A

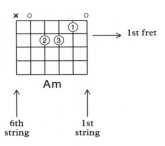

Ex. B

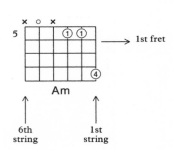

(i)   The vertical lines represent the strings.
(ii) The horizontal lines represent the frets.
(iii) A circle with a number inside shows where a finger should be pressed, and which finger is to be used.
(iv) X indicates that a string is not to be played.
(v)   O indicates that a string is open.
(vi) Ex. A shows a chord in the first position. When a chord is played higher up the fingerboard, the number on the left of the box indicates the position. (Ex. B is in the 5th position).

Rhythm Guitar Chords

The fingering and position of a chord is often based on the chords which precede and/or follow it. Although the chord shapes given are the most suitable for the pieces, occasionally a different chord position may be more convenient.

Note positions for the electric guitar

Note positions for frets 1–4

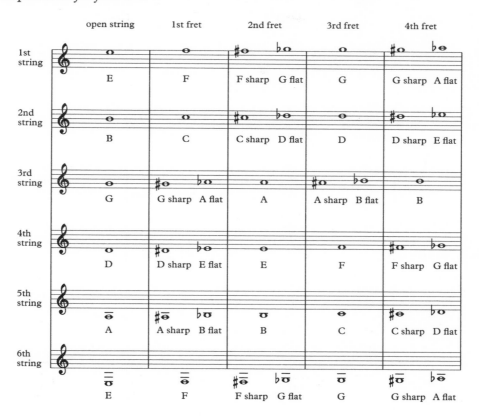

Note positions for frets 5–8

Note positions for frets 9–12

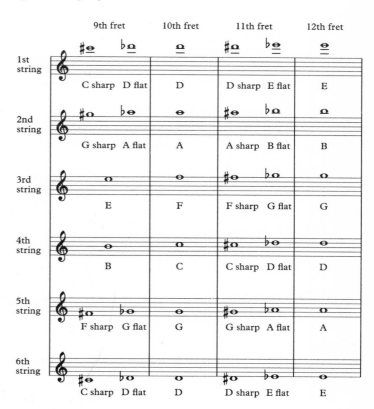

Note positions for bass guitar

Note positions for frets 1–4

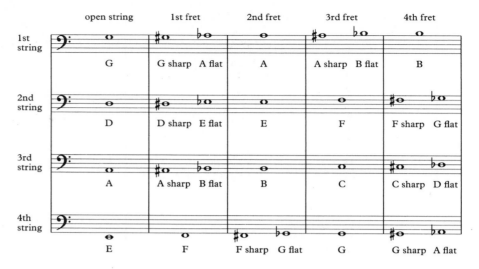

Note positions for frets 5–8

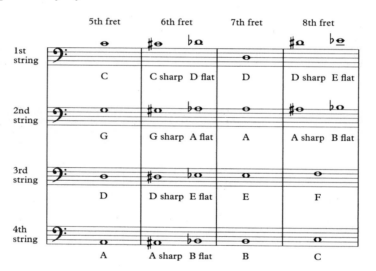

Note positions for frets 9–12

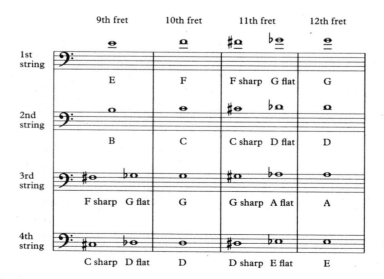